Goldilocks and the Three Bea

Characters: Three Bears, Goldilocks, and W
          (who mime the story and dance

Instrumental Parts: Pianoforte (adult performer)
                  Descant recorders (using notes G to D′ only)
                  Tuned and untuned percussion

The story is told and sung by children
The operetta is suitable for Infants or Lower Juniors

Duration 35 minutes

A separate recorder/percussion part is on sale

At the beginning of the operetta the three bears are seen asleep in their
cottage, which may be on two levels, the higher one representing the
bedroom. It is fairly dark, for it is night-time. Around the cottage, in
the wood, other animals are asleep too. A solitary badger may prowl
around during the song 'In the wood'. The singers and percussionists sit,
surrounding the scene and facing the cottage, ready to help tell the
story. The recorder players should be grouped together near the piano.
Groups of children may share the narration, while the actors mime
the story.

Notes for performance

1. Most of the percussion and recorder parts are optional, and may be easily omitted (obvious exceptions being the percussion parts in the Overture, and the recorders in 'The bears' walking song').
2. There is no reason why additional percussion should not be added in performance.
3. Other suitable music may be substituted for 'Dance of the woodland animals', if considered desirable.
4. A child, appropriately dressed, may represent the 'sun'.
5. Throughout the operetta, the woodland animals may join in the singing.
6. Props needed are as follows:
   (a) A 'house' for the bears, with a table
   (b) Three porridge bowls, spoons, chairs, and beds of different sizes
   (c) Imitation trees (etc.) for the wood
   (d) Costumes or part-costumes for the animals and Goldilocks

Contents

The purchase or hire of this work does not convey the right to perform, permission for which must be obtained from the publishers.

GOLDILOCKS AND THE THREE BEARS

Words and Music by
MAURICE BAILEY

1. Overture

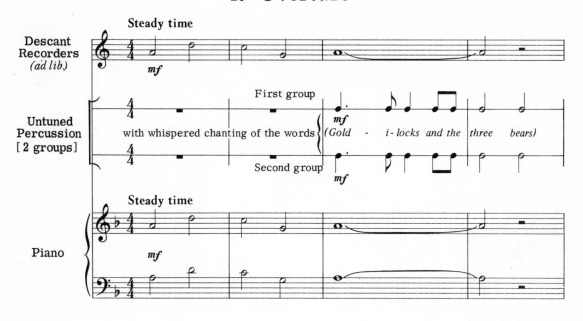

Printed in Great Britain

OXFORD UNIVERSITY PRESS, MUSIC DEPARTMENT, 37 DOVER STREET, LONDON W1X 4AH

NARRATOR: This is the story of
Goldilocks and the Three Bears.

NARRATOR: The three bears live in a pretty cottage in the middle of a wood. Father Bear has a deep, gruff voice.......*(sounds on 'low' instruments)*......., Mother Bear has a voice that is not deep, not high, but somewhere in between.......*(sounds on 'medium' instruments)*......., and Baby Bear has a high, squeaky voice.......*(sounds on 'high' instruments)*.

But, at the moment, the bears are not saying anything at all. They are asleep. It is very early morning, and it is still dark. We must wait for the sun to rise before our story can begin............

2. In the wood

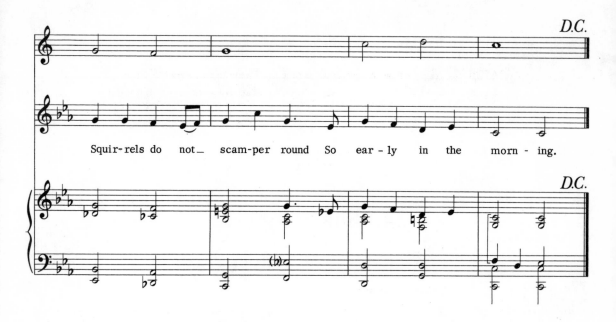

Squir-rels do not— scam-per round So ear-ly in the morn - ing.

2. Flowers, sleeping through the night,
   Petals closed very tight;
   They will open when it's light
   So early in the morning.

3. There is just a gentle breeze
   Rocking nests in the trees;
   Badger's out, but no one sees
   So early in the morning.

4. In the cottage, all three bears
   Late last night, said their prayers;
   Sleeping now, they have no cares
   So early in the morning.

NARRATOR: But now the night is over, and it is time for the sun to rise. Here it is, now!

(The 'sun' appears from behind the cottage, or wall, and the hall becomes much lighter. As this happens, we hear the 'Sunrise' music.)

2*a.* Sunrise music

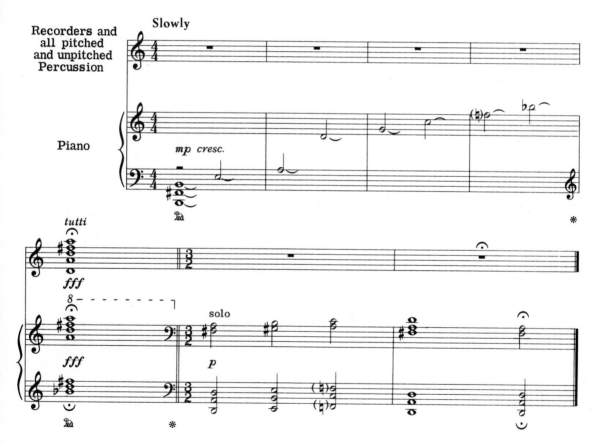

NARRATOR: There! The sun is filling the whole world with light! Now we can see the cottage and the wood very well.

    As the sunlight streams through the windows of the bears' house, it sings a little song to wake them up.

3. Wake up, sleepy bears!

Wake up, sleep-y bears! The day has just be-gun, It's time for break-fast!

1. Wash your-self and brush your fur, Come on now, it's time to stir! Fa-ther Bear, you must get up, and Mo-ther too!

2. Jump up now, there's lots to do, You have slept the whole night through! Ba-by Bear, it's time to start an-oth-er day!

NARRATOR: Gradually, all the other animals and birds in the wood wake up too.
Now Mother Bear is getting breakfast. She is making some porridge. Bears love porridge!

4. All bears like porridge!

Bet-ter than ba-con and eggs, Bet-ter than but-ter and toast,

Bet-ter than the Sun - day roast, — All bears like por-ridge! They
(2). They

8

NARRATOR: The bears sit down to eat the porridge, but—it's too hot! What shall they do while it is getting cool? Father Bear says, 'Why not go out for a walk?'
All three bears like walking in the wood, so, leaving the porridge on the table, off they go. They are so happy that they sing as they walk.

5. The bears' walking song

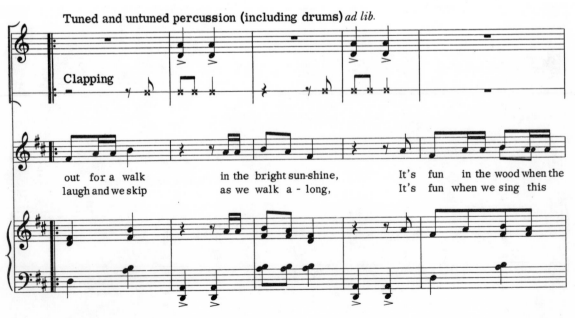

out for a walk   in the bright sun-shine,   It's fun in the wood when the
laugh and we skip   as we walk a - long,   It's fun when we sing this

wea-ther is fine,
mer- ry song, } Tra la la la la! We're three hap-py bears!

Recorders

Voices

Drums

2. We

(By the end of the song, the bears are out of sight.)

NARRATOR: Now the bears have gone, and the other animals, feeling happy and excited when they feel the warm, friendly sunshine, start to dance and play.

6. Dance of the woodland animals
Instrumental Rondo

(Triangles)

(Drums)

mf

NOTE: [a] The Xylophone part can be omitted, unless there is a competent player available.

[b] Other parts can be altered, simplified or (in most cases) dispensed with.

NARRATOR: Suddenly, the animals stop dancing, and the timid ones run back to their homes. Somebody is coming! It's a little girl, and her name is Goldilocks.

7. Poor little Goldilocks

1. Poor lit - tle Gold - i-locks, lost in a wood,
2. She sees a cot - tage and knocks at the door,

For she has done what no lit - tle girl should;
For she's too wear - y to walk an - y more;

She wand - ered off with-out say - ing a word;
No - bod - y an - swers, she'll just peep in - side;

Now she can't find her way home!
Why is there no - one at home?

(1st verse: *Goldilocks wanders through the wood towards the cottage.*)
(2nd verse: *Goldilocks goes inside and looks around.*)

Glockenspiel

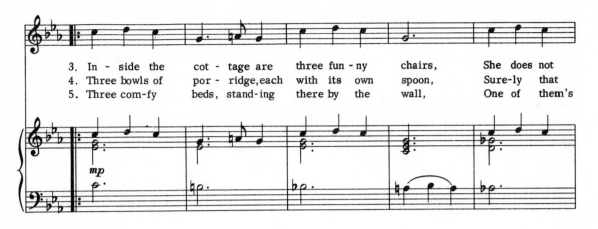

3. In - side the cot - tage are three fun - ny chairs, She does not
4. Three bowls of por - ridge, each with its own spoon, Sure-ly that
5. Three com-fy beds, stand-ing there by the wall, One of them's

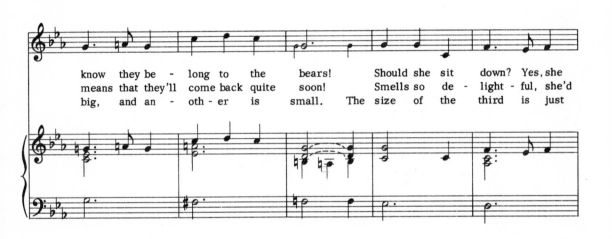

know they be - long to the bears! Should she sit down? Yes, she
means that they'll come back quite soon! Smells so de - light - ful, she'd
big, and an - oth - er is small. The size of the third is just

is ve - ry tired, Walk-ing so far from her home! ____
just like a taste, Hur - ry be - fore they come home! ____
some-where be - tween, She'll have a short rest, then go home! ____

3. *(She tries the chairs)*
4. *(She tries the porridge)*
5. *(She tries the beds)*

(Daddy's) 'It's too high!'
'It's too hot!'
'It's too hard!'

Glockenspiel

(Mummy's) 'It's too wide!'
'It's too cold!'
'It's too soft!'

3 - 4 verses:

(3. *(Baby Bear's chair breaks.)*
(4. 'This is just right' *(She eats porridge)*

(Long pause for 'business'.)

Last verse:

'This bed is just right!' *(She goes to sleep)*

NARRATOR: Poor Goldilocks! She was so tired and lonely! Now that she is asleep on Baby Bear's bed, all the animals in the wood are coming to peep at her through the window. The braver and bigger ones come first, and then the timid ones. They have never seen a little girl like Goldilocks before!

8. The peeping tune

1 Creep - ing, creep - ing to the lit - tle cot - tage,
2 Keep - ing, keep - ing oh so ve - ry qui - et!

Tread - ing soft - ly, must not make a sound!
They can see that Gold - i - locks is there;

Peep - ing, peep - ing through the cur - tained win - dows,
Sleep - ing, sleep - ing in the pret - ty bed - room,

All the wood-land an - i - mals are gath - 'ring round.
All the wood-land an - i - mals just stand and stare.

pp

NARRATOR: But here come the bears, back from their walk, still singing their song. When the other animals hear them, they run away from the cottage because they are rather scared of the big bears!

(Repeat No. 5 'The bears' walking song' as the bears return from their walk.)

NARRATOR: Now they have arrived back at the cottage, and go inside. But what is this? Somebody has been sitting in each of their chairs!

9. Somebody's been sitting in my chair!

1. Some - bod - y's been sit - ting in my chair! _____ And
2. Some - bod - y's been tast - ing my por - ridge! _____ And

Who's been sit-ting in my chair and bro-ken it to bits?
Who's been tast-ing my por - ridge and eat - en it all up?

Grum! Grum! Hum, hum, hum! These three bears are ve - ry glum!

Grum! Grum! Hum, hum, hum! These three bears are glum!

3. Some-bod - y's been ly - ing in my bed! _____ And

mp

some-bod-y's been ly-ing in mine!_____ And

cresc.

some-bod-y's been ly-ing in my bed, *(Spoken:)* And she's STILL THERE!

f

(add Percussion)

(The bears stare at Goldilocks,..She wakes up.............screams.............and runs away.)

p

fff

NARRATOR: So Goldilocks, not waiting to see whether the bears are friendly or not, runs away through the wood. *(Pause)*

Now, our story could end there, with the bears looking unhappy, and Baby Bear wishing that Goldilocks had stayed to play with him.

But perhaps Goldilocks *will* come back to see if the bears are friendly, and perhaps, if she does, the bears and the other animals in the wood will be so pleased, that they will all want to dance together. Let us wait and see........

(After a short expectant pause, Goldilocks does indeed return, to be greeted by the bears outside their cottage. The other animals, forgetting their fear of the bears, come out of hiding, ready to join the final dance, which can be of a more formal nature than the previous one. If desired, only the chorus need be sung.)

10. Finale

1. Gold - i - locks has come back to vis - it the three bears, ___
2. Ba - by Bear says that Gold - i - locks is his play - mate, ___

(Glock. echo)

When she walks in the wood their com-pa-ny she shares; ____
When her mum-my knows, will she say she can stay late? ____

Xylophone

She is sor-ry she ran a-way from the three bears! ____
Let her sleep at the cot-tage of her new play-mate! ____

The three bears and Gold - i - locks are now the best of friends, The three bears and Gold - i - locks are now the best of friends!

Printed in England by West Central Printing Co. Ltd., London and Suffolk